The Red Cart

by **Anne Giulieri**
illustrated by David Lorenzo

"I am going to play,"
said Duck.
"I can pull the red cart."

3

"Look!" said Hen.
"I can see a red cart.
I can go in the red cart."
Shhhh!

4

"I can go
in the red cart too,"
said Goat.
Shhhh!

6

"Look!" said Sheep.
"I can see a red cart.
I can go in the red cart."
Shhhh!

"I can go
in the red cart too,"
said Mouse.

Shhhh!

11

"Oh no!" said Duck.
"I cannot pull
the red cart."

"Look!"
said Duck.
"The red cart
is going down!"

"We can play!" said Duck.

16